BOOKS BY

LILLIAN SMITH

STRANGE FRUIT
KILLERS OF THE DREAM
THE JOURNEY
NOW IS THE TIME
ONE HOUR
MEMORY OF A LARGE CHRISTMAS
OUR FACES, OUR WORDS

OUR FACES,

LILLIAN SMITH

OUR WORDS

W · W · NORTON & COMPANY · INC · NEW YORK

To the young in the Movement who wisely or
sometimes unwisely have risked their lives for
a way of freedom that will bring growth to all; and
to the older ones, whether in years or experience,
who have learned that freedom is a hard thing,
that change means inner as well as outer change,
that nonviolence has to do as much with truth as
with love: to all of these I dedicate the
monologues which reveal, I trust, some of the hopes
and dreams and triumphs, the complexities and
difficulties of creating new kinds of human
relationships with one's fast-changing world.

Thanks are due to the following for photographs

MATT HERRON, CHARLES MOORE, BILL STRODE
AND BURK UZZLE FROM BLACK STAR

KENNETH THOMPSON

UPI

SHEL HERSHORN FOR *Life* MAGAZINE

WIDE WORLD PHOTOS

BRADLEY CLARK

CHARLES BRITTIN

FREDERICK DOUGLAS DeVAN

Contents

It's a terrible sleep
when you can't wake up

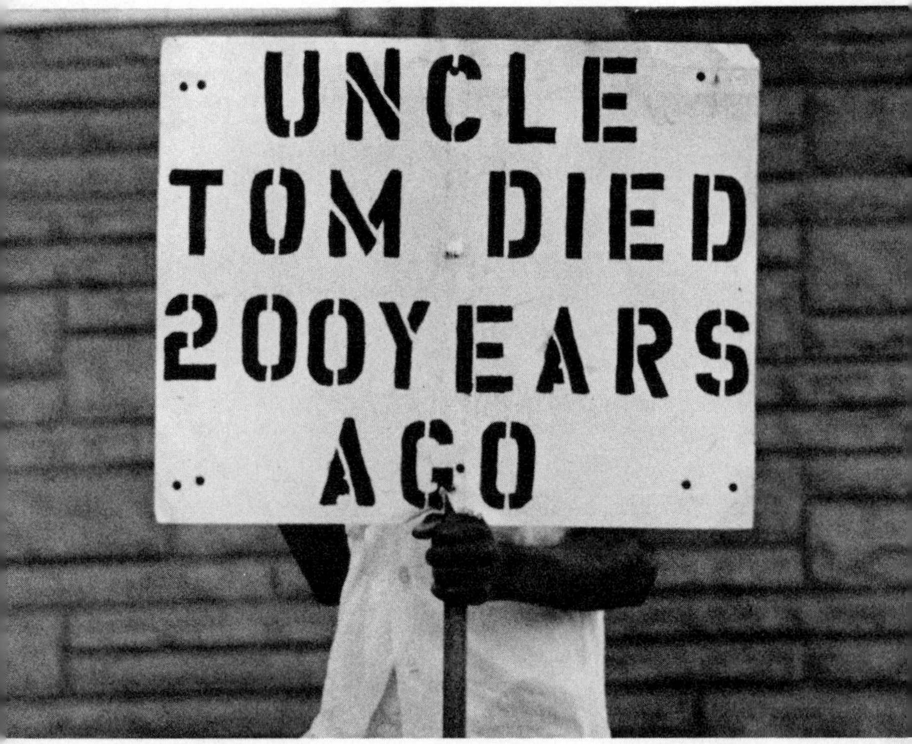
UNCLE
TOM DIED
200YEARS
AGO

WE SLEPT SO LONG. Everybody. When we walked we walked in our sleep; we went to school, a little —and slept through it; slept through cotton picking, through hunger, rain, cold; slept through moving North, even; we turned over, sat up, lay back down again.

It's a terrible sleep when you can't wake up. Now and then you feel there's something outside you, maybe a war or a flood or a freezing winter or a white man with a gun, maybe a mob, maybe a dead body in the path, or a face you'd better say howdy to, or a white lady you'd better step off the sidewalk for; or somebody tells a joke and you yap out in your sleep, you turn over, giggle, and slip back where you've been. Sometimes of a Sunday in church, at the singing, you almost wake up, or in a graveyard at a burying as you edge up to death you feel sleep about to leave you, or sometimes with a girl or a bottle of corn likker you get noisy, you laugh, belch, grunt, cuss loud, roll over and over. Now and then you sit up, look around, stare at the years; you see a star way off, but it always goes somewhere. You start sleep-walking again, past doors you can't enter, ten thousand, only you don't count, a hundred thousand you can't enter, but you don't care, past ten million things you can't touch, can't say, can't do, can't think, can't feel. You doze through it, turn over, sleep a little more, a little more, a little more.

That's the way it was. Then SOMETHING HAPPENED. Did Jesus call? did God shake us? did the earth tremble? did a trumpet blow? did the walls fall? why is everybody running? are they going somewheres? Come on you, we're going somewheres, yeah, git up, open your eyes, we're going somewheres, hurry, we're going somewheres, you gotta hurry, see? git up, and hurry or they'll leave us. Hurry . . .

**We were there, man, and
we knew we were there**

I MUST HAVE BEEN about sixteen when I saw that painting: a Negro boy, leaning against a big white post; every muscle in him limp, acquiescent; nothing to give out except yassir. I felt naked, stripped; I *was* that painting or it was me. This is the way you are, my body whispered, all Negroes are, my mind burned. I couldn't say, It's a stereotype, laugh it off; I couldn't even get mad, all my glands would do was pour out shame. I looked around to see what others thought. Most were just talking to each other, they didn't hear what it said.

I went out on the street, a car honked, I jumped out of its way, I wasn't looking. Something in me moved a little; now I was resenting that picture, not much, but some. A white man painted it, I told myself, even the artists lie about us, showing us limp, no fight, all time making us nothing. I walked two blocks, whistling something or other. Turned into a side street, walked on. Dammit, a half block from our house I looked straight at a Negro boy leaning against a post, muscles gone, soul gone, nothing to give out, nothing to fight back with.

I kept seeing it, that painting come alive: I'd meet

it at street corners, see it leaning against a railing or a lamp post, meet it as I cut through the alley: there it'd be, squatting, looking down at the dirt, spitting now and then, or lying flat hat over eyes, asleep. It turned into my private nightmare, hung on the edge of everything I did, or looked at.

And then in '61 I stopped seeing this Thing that whispered its kinship to me. It left me one Monday, when I was picketing on A——— street. We picketed a big restaurant, fifty-five of us. Godamighty, there we were in the dead center of White Town, picketing the biggest store on their biggest street. Man, we were there! And we knew we were there, and we knew what we were going to do there. We were there to get something that belonged to us; a gift from God and it had our names on it, a right we inherited from the Constitution and it had our names on it, too. No more yassir. We were saying No. No No No to closed public doors, to closed voting booths, to slum housing, to ignorance, to Jim Crow courts and their judges. No! And every time we said it the slimy nasty yassirs slid out of us and slunk down a past gone forever.

To tell the truth I sort of flipped when I realized all of that was GONE. Muscles told me so, bones shouted it, bodies moved sure of the next step, sure of the next encounter, sure of tomorrow.

A fellow next to me on the picket line said—kind of shook up by it all, "My God, they *see* us! We're real!" I laughed easy. Then I laughed big as a cop came near; he came up close, he watched me but he

didn't touch me, he just watched me, and from his face I knew he was looking at more than me, he saw a million, twenty million niggers with me. "Yes Mister," I said softlike to myself, "you're going to keep on seeing us until you stop seeing us as nigger; when we're sure you can see us as Americans, as human beings, then—well, we'll go back to school and get on with the business of living and we'll help you get on with the business of living, too, but we got to rub the yassir out of your ears, see? we've got to make you hear us say NO and we got to be sure you learn what it means. We don't hate you but we don't fear you, either; you see, we got something worth dying for and living for, we're lucky; you can't scare us, not even with your dogs, not even when *you* turn animal to keep us from being human. We got power, man. Yeah. Power to say NO, power to make you say YES, because history is with us, right is with us, economics is with us, science is with us, mercy and love and freedom are with us. We won't rub it in, bud; we won't make you say yassir but you've got to learn to say yes, and mind your manners when you say it. Right?

A cup of coffee

To GO BACK FOUR YEARS: that day, I'd been reading. *Franny and Zooey*. Everybody was reading it in our dorm. There were other books on Bill's shelf and mine, the usual things: Camus' *Sisyphus*, Dylan Thomas, Mailer, Sartre; I had just read *Borstal Boy*. We were English majors. I was trying out for an Ionesco play in French. All this is to suggest, I guess, that I didn't go in for the racial stuff, "sociological problems," our English prof called it. I hadn't even read Dick Wright. I just didn't like race talk.

My uncle kept his life raw with it. He was that kind, couldn't pass up a slight. Had to bleed. Active in NAACP. Always fighting the white man. Before I was born he was going after the Negro's rights. Once, I was about six or so, he said to me, "Tell me, do you know who you are?" I saw Mama look up, put her hand out to stop him, then as suddenly, she went back to stringing the beans for supper.

"I'm Jim," I said.

"Jim who?"

I told him.

"That's not important."

"Yes, it is," Mama said. "Jim is a person, he has a

name, and he's going to make us proud of it, some day."

Uncle laughed. I thought it a mean laugh; maybe it was just an unhappy one. "Your mama don't want you to learn the facts of life," he said. "The most important fact for you, Jim, is that you are a Negro." He looked at Mama (she's his sister) as if to say, You can lie to him but not to me. "You're not a nigger—and don't you ever let anybody call you one. But you are a Negro. And the sooner you learn it the better. You're as good as anybody technically, but you are not, actually, until you get your rights as an American. White folks are not going to give them to you even though they belong to you. Remember: they stole 'em from you. Remember: folks don't like to return what they steal. You'll have to take 'em back. And to do it you'll have to work to get them; you can never let up, never for one minute let up."

Mama said, "Jim and I—we look at it another way. Jim's a human being, you're one, too (though you're not acting like one now)." She smiled. Uncle snorted. "Jim knows he's human—much like the other two and a half billion humans across the earth. He knows he's an individual and different from others; he knows it is good to be different and every human being has a right to be different. But color is a false difference; it is not important to Jim nor to me. It shouldn't be to anybody."

Uncle looked at me. Things were being said I couldn't hear, I felt them whizzing between the two. Uncle's voice snagged on his words, "You believe all

24

this, what your mother is saying?"

"Yes sir."

"Well, young man, what you going to do with all these fine notions?"

"He's going to grow up to be a real man, intelligent, decent, hardworking, who will leave a good mark on the world, I hope," said Mama.

"Ha!" said Uncle. "Just like that! Easy, too, huh?" My pup began chasing a chicken, I ran to help him. I didn't like Uncle's voice and I shied away from him after that day.

Mom works in the branch library, called the James Weldon Johnson Branch. (It is integrated, today, but it wasn't four years ago.) I used to go down most every afternoon to read and look around. We had a lot of good juveniles at home, too; of course they were about white children, no little Negroes, but I accepted that. I guess I vaguely thought it strange not to put little Negroes in books, too—but it wasn't a hurting thought. Mom took me to the plays and concerts at the Negro college; I'd go sound to sleep but I liked going. I accepted my world; I didn't know any other; most children accept the world they're born into, even when it is a place where earthquakes play around.

After high school, I went to the college here at home. I lived in the dorm—and that day I am telling about, I was reading *Franny and Zooey,* and I was with it. I wasn't thinking, "I'm a Negro and all this is alien to me. It wasn't, it was real and human. A guy named Dan was talking to my roommate. I heard him

25

say, "My mom was just getting over flu, see? And she'd been shopping all morning. She'd bought about fifty-five dollars' worth of stuff; she was matching a spool of thread when suddenly everything began to black out. She knew if she could sit down a few minutes and have a cup of coffee she'd be OK. But where in that store or anywhere else downtown could she get it! She fainted. They had a time: somebody got her ammonia, somebody found a cot for her, and somebody else brought her a cup of coffee."

Bill laughed. "One way to get it. It's not funny, Dan. But there's a terrible irony—"

Dan nodded. "When it's your own mother you don't think about irony."

I closed the book. To hell with *Franny and Zooey* . . .

If Mom was tired and needed a cup of coffee where could she get it downtown? Dammit to hell, where could she get it? Jesus Christ! She could buy out the store and still couldn't buy one cup of coffee and sit down quietly and drink it. You never thought about it before—how about going to the john—did they let her go to a restroom—

I saw Mom, suddenly. Right there, standing in front of my whole life. Gray-eyed, gentle, poised. Always so quietly poised. My God, where did her serenity come from! She'd never said a bitter word in her life against the whites, not to me; and she wasn't a hand-kerchief-head, either; talk about white folks giving you back your "dignity"—Mom's dignity couldn't have been taken from her, it went down to the center of her soul. I saw all this. I saw all she'd tried to keep me from looking at, cesspools and stinking ways, dirty alleys in streets and minds—Mom all the time turning me toward books, music, poetry, drama, ideas, science, hoping, I guess, that I'd never catch on to what it was really about. She couldn't stand hate—I guess she didn't want me poisoned by it.

"Dan," I said, "let's make em open up those places."

"OK by me," said Dan.

That's the way the revolution started for us. We were suddenly *there*. In it. We'd never been a black boy, like Dick Wright down in Mississippi. We'd never felt invisible, way Ralph Ellison felt. We never felt we were Nothing; I was always sure I was Something. Well, I admit it: we'd been mighty sheltered; our race had never had it so good, I guess, as the middle-class Negro in some of the upper-South cities had it when I was growing up. I'd never seen a Klansman in my life; had never seen a race murder, never heard a mob on the loose. I knew such things happened, read about them but I guess I pushed them off. *They didn't get on my mind.* I knew there were places I couldn't go but having the college we were able to enjoy many advantages even the whites in our city didn't have. Somehow my pride never got tangled up in it; oh, I knew I couldn't enter certain places but I honestly believe I didn't worry about this much more than the average middle-class white southern kid worries who knows he can't join a millionaires' club; I knew about Negro slums, Harlem, South Side but thought about it in the same way most white boys think about slums and bad housing for whites. I was *sound asleep,* let me settle for that. My mother was a lady to her fingertips; I guess I pretended she was exactly like any white lady with access to the same civilities and courtesies.

Well—we were waking up. We dressed in our Sunday clothes to look like the gentlemen we made like we were, took our Bibles and school books and started our sit-in. But before we sat in, we did read up on what the others had done in Greensboro and Tallahassee. We knew we'd better get with this nonviolence thing. We didn't have time to read Martin Buber or Gandhi or Thoreau but we did take time out to read Martin Luther King—all about redemption through suffering, "absorbing" the cruelties of others . . . conciliation . . . compassion. I read it. Dan read it.

"My God," Dan said, "what the hell is redemption?"

I stared at him. There was nothing in *Franny and Zooey* about redemption. Somebody said—Bill, I think—"maybe we'd better read Camus' *The Fall.*" We decided we didn't have time. We wouldn't say it but I think we felt we'd better get going before we lost our nerve. "We'll get redeemed, later," Bill said solemnly, "we'd better go sit now." Dan was staring hard at me, it made me tremble, I felt things turning upsidedown. "Let's get going," I said. Voice sort of loud.

Well, we got going and sat in at Walgreen's. Don't know why we picked that one but we did. Maybe

because we knew it was a chain store and might be more sensitive to pressures—but I don't know, we actually weren't doing much thinking. We walked to the counter, sat down, opened our books. Bill opened the Bible—and read it, too. I had my physics textbook; read one paragraph sixteen times without knowing what was in it. The white girl behind the counter, awfully young, turned pink then deathly white. She didn't say a word. Bill looked up, smiled, said quietly, "We'd like some coffee, please, and some doughnuts." She swallowed, swallowed again, shook her head. "I can't," she said. She wasn't mean. I felt sorry for her. "Please go away," she whispered, "they won't let me serve you." We sat there.

Pretty soon, two or three white kids came in, stared at us, one sat down next to me, hummed something, got up, walked out. We kept on reading. Some more came in; we didn't turn round to see but they were making a lot of noise. Then it happened: that cigarette; the goon stuck the burning thing into my back. Sit tight, don't move, take it; this is nonviolence, I told myself, you have to take it. A white guy came in, knocked the cigarette out of the other guy's hand; there was scuffling back of me; I didn't turn. A cop came in. Walgreen's closed the counter. We left.

That's how we started. Three weeks later, the lunch counter opened to everybody. By then, we were sitting in at Kress's. There were about twenty-five or more students helping us now, and more high-school kids than we needed; the high-school kids just poured into the movement, completely unafraid, having a ball, but serious, too, deepdown.

We felt we had to hold meetings now to decide what to do, what not to do; we had to learn you can't lose your temper, you can't talk back, you can't hit back; you keep everything under control. Two of the college men couldn't make it; we told them to stay out of things until they could control their feelings; the high school kids were cool, and they listened. "You got to feel compassionate toward the whites," a worker from CORE told us; at our request he had come to train us. So we talked about compassion, forgiveness, talked about absorbing evil through our own suffering. "You'll find it works," the Core adviser told us; "if a white has any good in him, he'll respond to compassion and friendly talk; you got to remember that you can hate evil without hating the man who does the evil; it's like a doctor treating the evil of smallpox without hating the man who has it."

"Yeah," said one kid, "but you'd better fear that smallpox." Everybody laughed.

"Sure," said the teacher of nonviolence, "you've got to have sense; be wary, be shrewd, nobody was more shrewd than Gandhi, don't be reckless; but remember: negative nonviolence is not enough; it's got to be positive; you feel all the time that the other man, the one fighting you, can be redeemed; he's got to feel something good in you."

This was tough on most of us; we didn't want to be cowards; we felt it would do us a world of good to punch a white bully in the nose; we wondered if these goons possessed souls; maybe terror had to be

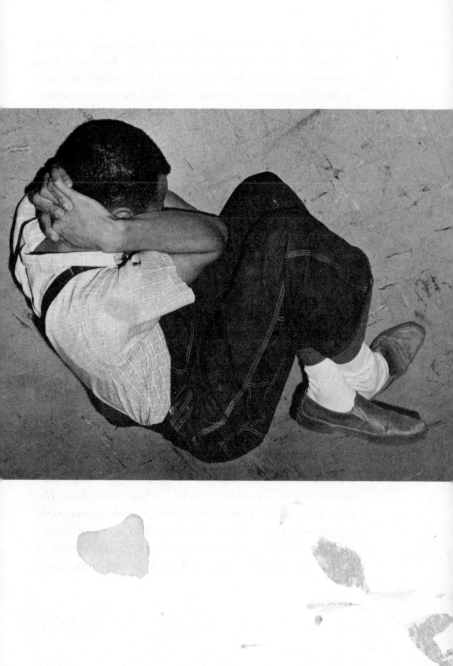

met with terror; maybe those cops actually couldn't respond to love. We talked about this; but we knew, somewhere in us, that strategically a minority can't change things by violence, it would be suicide to try; and we began to see that while one goon may fail to respond to conciliation and friendly reason and this thing we called "love," hundreds of thousands of the public, white and Negro looking on, would begin to respond, begin to understand; and we dimly saw that when this happens change comes, real change. For this is the beginning of dialogue, of response of one human to another.

Well, back to the Kress business. Six girls were sitting in with us, very brave and gay. There was a lot of laughter and singing; maybe no movement in the world's history has ever been such a singing movement as this one. But things were getting tougher. A mean editorial appeared in the morning paper; the editor couldn't grasp the basic idea of truth and compassion in human relations; he honestly didn't believe we as Americans should protest the lack of our civil rights; he seemed to think we should just keep on as our grandfathers had done; but the editor was caught fast in the first decade of the century.

A week later, Kress's opened up. We moved on from Kress's to picketing the biggest department store in town. Somehow, I got in jail. That hurt Mom. *Her* son. They sent us there because we had "trespassed." I wanted to say, "Mom, I'm in jail so you can have a cup of coffee when you want one." I didn't say it. That cup of coffee had metamorphosed into everything Negroes lacked that was rightfully theirs as human beings. It looked like we'd have to open up the whole city, the whole region; then we'd have to go North and help them open up things there, too.

Now, here I am in Mississippi; working on a literacy program for the Negro sharecroppers in the Delta, getting them registered to vote; grassroots stuff. (Oh yes—somewhere along the way we stopped wearing our Sunday clothes. We wear jeans now.) We've collected thousands of books, trying to fix up centers where they can come and read. There're no real schools for the colored kids down here. Parents can't read or write, most of them. Money? That's funny. You don't sit in restaurants in a place like this. Where would they get money to go to a restaurant? Where would they get clothes to wear? They don't have wants like that. They *need. Need everything.* This is zero. You begin here in the mud and dust at nothing and inch up. Got to. No other way. Whites are about as bad off as the Negroes. It is like the Indian villages, a Hindu visitor told us, only maybe worse; more fear, more pressure on the Negroes; hostile police. I didn't know all this existed, had no idea it could exist. In college, we didn't talk about these things, we read *Waiting for Godot.* What you reckon these kids here in the Delta are waiting for; I wish I knew. They're born and then they start waiting, waiting. Sometimes at night, you're riding along one of these bumpy rough roads through the fields, everything stretching away from you, sky tilted, stars spilling out of space, now and then a light way off, a

35

thousand shadows where the shacks are. And you think, They're full of children, real honest-to-God children, and they're all waiting for something to happen here in our country, in the United States; and suddenly the waiting is a ghost choking me and I fight it, I shake it off whispering, Tomorrow I'll teach a kid to read: "This is a book; I want to know what is in it." One inch; one inch up.

**The search for excellence
takes us to strange places**

I WAS TWELVE WHEN the Supreme Court decided segregated schools wouldn't do. I took it for granted that before long things would be different at our school. But nothing happened. And nothing much happened anywhere. In our school, some of the kids told more rough jokes than usual, repeated more words that would hurt Negroes if they heard, some said they'd fight back if desegregation came, they'd show those colored kids what was what. A lot of us didn't like this talk but we didn't do anything. Most of us wouldn't have minded integration. But we didn't do anything. We didn't tell our principal how we felt, or the teachers, or the school boards, or those white kids who were muttering the nasty jokes. We were scared. Not scared of the integration experiment but scared to act freely according to how we really felt; scared of those mobs folks talk about, scared that Negroes, if they came to our school, would get hurt, scared of the unknown, I suppose. So, we made ourselves indifferent. We tried to tell ourselves we felt all right about it but after all, why was it our business to speak out!

People away from here asked why? Why didn't you

do something! Remember how the commentators asked it over and over? And nobody could say. I was dumb, I couldn't say. But now I know this is what segregation has done to us whites: it has paralyzed us; we don't dare act out what we know is right. We don't dare say what we know should be said. We let the demagogues say anything but we are mute. Oh I know: we are scared of the goons and the ghosts and the monsters segregation has bred. For a hundred years, the nice people sat here and let politicians and the power structure that supported them chain our minds with their lies until we couldn't think straight. Listen to intelligent white people talk on this subject! Most of them lie and they don't care; they don't want to find the truth, they just repeat sleazy excuses they've heard before. People, even with Ph.D.'s, can't think critically; half of them end up talking about mongrelizing or states' rights. And when you say the states don't have any rights, read your Constitution, they stare as if you're crazy.

Oh well—I was as bad as the rest. I wanted to do the right thing, I wanted to be decent, I wanted to become something you might call a human being but I was scared. Later, at college (I went North to school) I heard Martin Luther King speak; then I heard Bayard Rustin; I went down to New York to hear them; then I had an interview with Anna Arnold Hedgman. I began to read. I was watching what was happening in Africa, I kept up with the sit-ins. After last summer—it hit me hard, everything hit me—I thought, Join the movement; get out and help break

42

down the segregation system; do it quick before you get scared; picket, sit-in—you've got to, to save your own soul. And I did it.

And it wasn't long before I was in jail. The cops are rough on white girls, rougher than on Negro girls, and they're rougher with Negro girls than with Negro men. Well, there I was and they had put me by myself. I'm not very brave. I was more scared than a white girl from the North who was jailed at the same time. She went in laughing. I admired her but I knew she didn't know what was ahead.

Or maybe I was scared from a lifetime of being warned, Don't do that, don't speak out, don't take a stand, you can't, something awful will happen. I don't know. I had heard the stories of how a matron in one jail had made some of the girls in the movement strip naked, then she let other inmates hit them, make foul jokes, etc.

I held as steady as I could; walked back and forth in my cell; there was a small window, I stood there looking out. And to keep from sliding into panic I sang the songs of the movement, *We Shall Overcome, Freedom,* and the rest of them.

I am from a Methodist family. Pretty soon I was singing old Sunday School songs. Funny, how deep-down they go in you. I was humming *Wash Me and I Shall be Whiter than Snow,* thinking of those old days—sin sin sin—everything, nearly, was a sin except segregation. Whiter than snow, that means we are pure; dark, that means they are impure—how asinine can the human mind get! Segregation, a holy ritual, more meaningful than the Lord's Supper. You couldn't question it. You bowed down and worshiped the Whiteness it ritualized. It scared me to think this. I had read it before; now in that jail I believed it. We've lost God. We've surrounded ourselves with godlets; our white skin is the # 1 god we worship. When you've got white skin you don't even need a soul. I tried to laugh; I cried a little.

Mississippi . . . that is where I was. Bleak and beautiful and terrible, that state. Beyond tragedy. What holocaust will they bring on themselves? Will they push things as far as did the Nazis? Can they and still remain a part of our nation? Is there no way—

Someone was at the door. The cop. I had on my shirt and jeans, just as I was when he arrested me. He arrested me for breaking a traffic rule, he said. He knew I was working with "the niggers" so he took me to jail. No accident, no one hurt, nothing had happened, I hadn't even broken a minor traffic law. But things are not real, here; truth is an irrelevance; I have never met a truthful cop; there may be some somewhere, I'm sure there are a few in Atlanta, or Richmond, maybe in North Carolina or Tennessee; but I have never come near one in the movement. He began to talk. I tried not to hear; the words were mostly words I can't say aloud. He wanted to know what nigger I had slept with the night before. Was it fun? Did he screw me better than white men can? "You must have some excuse, a damned good one, for going out and sittin-in with these niggers! They

44

pay you for it, do they, at nights?"

I stood there, humming. I didn't dare stop. My heart was skipping, I was scared, outraged. There was nobody to call to for help. This is the worst part of segregation, this foul obscenity that rots white people's minds away. You feel minds are crawling with lice that have crept out of the rotten dirty places in our lives. And cops seem to have more than their share. Why? Why do we have these people for policemen? Is it true the world over that the dregs are the police? I don't know. They should be the very best, men we believe in and admire for their good judgment, their moral cleanness, their self discipline. But in the South, it doesn't turn out that way. Down here, most of them seem obsessed about "mixed children." Millions of mixed children: sex and sin wrapped up in a dirty cloth called segregation. But it is all right just so the kids are "illegal." A "legitimate" mixed-race child—ah, there's the horror, the taboo! A child born from a holy marriage? Oh no, that's terrible!

I couldn't sleep after he walked away. It was so still. All the big sounds deathly still. But a thousand thin noises ran along my nerve endings. I was cold, shaking cold. I clung to the window, I clung to outer space, hung on desperately, trying to forget everything behind me: the South I love and fear, its sweet stench, its gentle terrors, its sudden naked horrors —and its desire "to be good." And its apathy—aching to be good and yet unable to move.

Why can't the warmhearted, intelligent southerners change? Why can't they move? why can't they speak

out? Daddy, why haven't you spoken out? You have
nice feelings, you didn't join a White Citizens' Coun-
cil, you wouldn't lynch or dynamite anyone, you
wouldn't push and scrouge (or would you?), you
don't say "nigger," but you're against the Public Accommodations measure, you think a city has a holy
right to close itself up against a part of the citizenry
because of color; you think property rights are more
important than human rights, don't you? You're really
against the entire Civil Rights bill, aren't you?
"They're taking away our rights," you say, "they're
tearing up the Constitution!" You say this, my father
whom I adore, and yet you read Plato; you're supposed to be a kind of local authority on the old
Greeks, all time quoting Aeschylus. How can you?
how can you . . . how can you . . . I'm crying, I'm
a little girl crying because she wants a brave, honest
father who seeks the truth *of his time* not the Greeks'
time, who can look beyond this awful mess we're in.
You went to Harvard—and yet you fall for the lies
Mr. Rich White told Mr. Poor White long ago, to
keep him satisfied with poverty and sharecropping,
and all the rest of it. How can you? Don't you know
why all that was said? don't you know it was to keep
the poor whites from demanding *their* rights as Americans? Do you need me to tell you that is why Mr.
Rich White handed them a drug instead of bread?
a tranquilizer for their hungry souls to feed on—and
now it has driven some of them mad.

I love you. That is what hurts. I admire so much of
you; when you're off this subject of race you are sane

47

and erudite and charming. And Mother—she does more about the problem than you do, Dad, but she does it secretly; she's afraid of what you'll say. That isn't fair to her, there's an edge of you that troubles her, too; she worships you but there is a little edge she keeps the bright light off of.

Last summer, when the trouble happened in Birmingham, in our hometown, you didn't do anything. Even after the bombings, even after those four little girls were killed, you didn't do anything. Not a damned thing! You're respected, you're prominent, you're popular, you're a member of the best clubs, you're on the Board of Stewards of our church and you didn't do a thing to help, to say This is Wrong. Oh I know, you said at home, That's pretty bad—but you didn't say it where anyone else could hear. What could you have done? You and Mother could have got in your car and called on the heartbroken parents, you could have said, "We're sorry." That one little thing might have unbound you. Freed you.

Mother says you think I sat-in just to embarrass you, to shame you. She says you think I deliberately got myself put in jail. Maybe I did! Maybe I did just that! If I did, I was wrong; that's a poor reason for fighting for any good cause. But whatever my motive, I had to do *something!* Maybe I screamed to drown out your silence. And so I ended up in a Mississippi jail, listening to a dirty lowdown cop talking about "niggers screwing" me—me, your Vassar-educated, summer-camp-trained daughter who loves poetry and philosophy and art and human beings and the excel-

lence her father told her always to search for. But
the search for excellence can be dangerous—it takes
us to strange places, sometimes, doesn't it, Dad?

What do we want?

You ask me what we want. And I say, Who are *we?* Some of us are Negro, some are white; many are students, young, yeah—but we're not the same: our minds fill with different thoughts, we love different things, want different futures, hate different people —maybe I don't mean that—yes, I guess I do—some of us hate like hell; oh we try not to but we hate. We fight it, some of us, we lie about it to ourselves, make like we're compassionate, make like we're willing to suffer to redeem our fellow Americans from evil, but —listen: when a dog is nipping your tail—hell, not even Gandhi could feel compassion. Dogs . . . ever think what that means? White men using animals as allies against their fellow human beings. Man—you get that? Get the significance? You better than a nigger, white man says to dog, go after him, go after that little kid! tear her to pieces! she's just a hunk of black flesh who's forgot to stay where she belongs; you're superior, you're a fine animal, you're our friend, we don't segregate you, it's the nigger we segregate.

There's something terrible about that. You feel it? It ought to hurt, ought to scare you if you really see what those cops and their bosses are doing. Human beings, all human beings, are different from animals —there's a profound and irreversible difference between animal and man. Talk about mongrelization . . . all human beings can breed with each other— they can because it is God's will that they do so if they want to; but a man can't lay with his dog and bring forth a living creature; yet dogs are used against *us*, the whites' fellowmen. This hurts. There's an irreversible difference. This hurts. See! I sound like I can't get out of the groove.—And I keep saying "irreversible" because I mean it: all human beings have a million things in common that no animal shares with them: speech, the power to make new things, the power to question, to search for meaning, to explore, discover —and the knowledge that we all must die; maybe that is the biggest difference of all, it's your shadow, you never shake it; and the power to think of historical time, that in itself makes you need something to steady you, if you think about it long enough: think how we go back and dig, not for a bone to gnaw as do the dogs but for a bone to study and maybe write a poem about, or use as a clue as we are putting a billion years of the past together; all this, our power to plan for the future, to paint, to write music. Wonder what'd happen if we'd get quiet all over the earth and think about this, what makes us human, for five minutes. Maybe we'd see each other different. But those cops—maybe I'll ask the next one who sticks an electric prod to my tail, maybe I'll just stop and say, "Socrates, what is a human being?" You reckon he does actually think a white skin makes a human being? It's all so crazy—

Oh, I know: plenty of Negroes don't know either. And some are in the movement: there because it gives them a chance to let out their resentment, a chance to defy that awful ghost, "white power." But deep in them, they know the real reasons, too; only they don't know words to say it right; they want what we all want, freedom to breathe, feel, think, move. White ghetto—black ghetto: both are mean places to grow a kid, as mean as the Mississippi delta, in a different way.

And, making things worse are the cops turning against their own kind and using animals to beat down their unarmed fellowmen. I used to go to church; well, I still go, my body goes, I'm not sure my heart goes anymore, I am messed up inside. But I have a feeling about blasphemy; and I say it is blasphemy for one human being to use dogs against another human being.

What's ruining the nonviolent movement, what's bringing out the hate that a little compassion and hope had sort of diluted, is the cruelty of these cops; the vicious extremes to which the powerful whites will go to maintain a system even they no longer profit from. But you can't help but think they are deliberately provoking us to violence. I said we were sort of naive. Well, we were. But you go out on the streets, unarmed mind you, having had a session with yourself in which you've prayed for self control, for the power to forgive, and then—here come those dogs. Whatever you are afterward, you're not naive.

Can't you laugh? somebody said. Jesus . . . laugh! Oh sure, once you're back home—if you don't land in jail as most of us do—you laugh to your family. Try to. Then that night you dream about those dogs —I reckon it went deep with me—you dream you're on the street, in front of a restaurant, say; and first, you see a lot of white faces staring at you, then the faces begin to twist with rage, terrible rage that's beyond words and then, face after face, they turn to snarling dogs, ears droop, mouths open, and now there's a hundred dogs after you and you're running running round the earth, round the earth and the dogs are at your tail and you run and choke and pant — And then, you wake up. And your heart is racing, and you're sweating and you feel you going to vomit and no words come—then finally you get still, you're sweating wet but you're still and you feel your soul is bleeding to death—your po' little ole soul, as your grandma might say, is bleeding to death.

And you're supposed to keep loving white folks, keep being patient and courteous and wait another hundred years for their convenience. And then, if some fool idiot who's black makes a crazy-wild suggestion like turning on all the water taps, white folks say, "Ain't you shamed? don't you know this is America and Americans don't do things like turning on water taps?"

This is the moment folks go raving crazy; some laugh for days and can't stop; raving, yeah, raving mad. And folks says, Why can't the leaders control "their people"? We are not the leaders' people—we're

57

America's people and America is letting us down down down down.

Oh I know—not all white people would turn the dogs on us. Not one in a thousand would do it. And I know it is not just the white southerners, they're using the dogs up North, too. And they used them in the war—and Hitler used them in concentration camps. But the millions who say they wouldn't do it let the hundreds have their way—and these hundreds are not white goons, they're the official police who are under the control of the mayor of the city and the chief of police.

Why don't decent people say something? Why the silence? why the passivity? They're not under Hitler, they're under President Johnson, and he is for us having our civil rights; I honestly believe he is. What are these people scared of? what their neighbors will say? what are they so loyal to? is it loyalty? is it a taboo they're too primitive to break? or are their souls already dead—and they don't know it. You can go to church with a dead soul inside you; you can give a lot of money to the church and still be what the Bible calls a "'whited sepulchre."

What is really wrong with our people! *Our people.* No, I didn't slip up. I meant that. That's the way I feel. Americans, black and white, are my people. Deep in my heart I feel this way. Maybe I should feel glad I feel this way—thankful that I don't automatically hate people because they're white. But I *don't* feel good; all this tears me to pieces—it's hell to love and hate white folks, but that's what I do:

my conscience, my reason say, You love them, you pity, you understand they, too, were born into this mess; but my heart says No! you hate them—not for the few who dynamite and kill but for the many who let these terrible things happen and don't move to stop them.

I struggle with this. I guess if you think, if you feel ambiguities, if you see evil and good braided together, you shouldn't get involved in life, much less involved in a revolution. You ought to go to Paris, and sit on the Left Bank and make like you're living in Proust's and Gide's time. That's just great—and you wouldn't have to go through the hell we're going through here in this so-called revolution.

Is it a revolution? I don't know. Certainly not a political one. Maybe it is a spiritual one: maybe; we started out hoping it would be something that would go deep into the soul of all our people, white and black, and change us so that our future could be different, richer, more open. But now—here we are hating; here we are talking about black this and black that—worse than the Mississippians with their whiteness. Is everything falling into a heap of ruins? It makes me want to cry when I remember how we colored kids started in the Movement, some of us naive, yes; but we were purehearted; some of us had mothers who had given us a deepdown security that pushed hate away. We were sort of beautiful black Galahads going forth in search of the twentieth century's Holy Grail—the lost Grail which we must find in order for us to live as human beings should. Well—

here we are, now, and some of us are not doing so well, are we.

Oh, yes—your question. What do we want? *Dignity*. Oh sure. As if dignity can be given! You grow it from deep inside you, or you don't have it. Our civil rights? Yes. But I want more. I'm beginning to see, I want more. I want a life where the human being is known for what he can be, where he can dream big and not feel like a fool. Pompous? Vague? Forget it. All I'd better say is this Movement has got my soul to aching. And it hurts. God . . . how it hurts.

**Memories: how sweet
and terrible!**

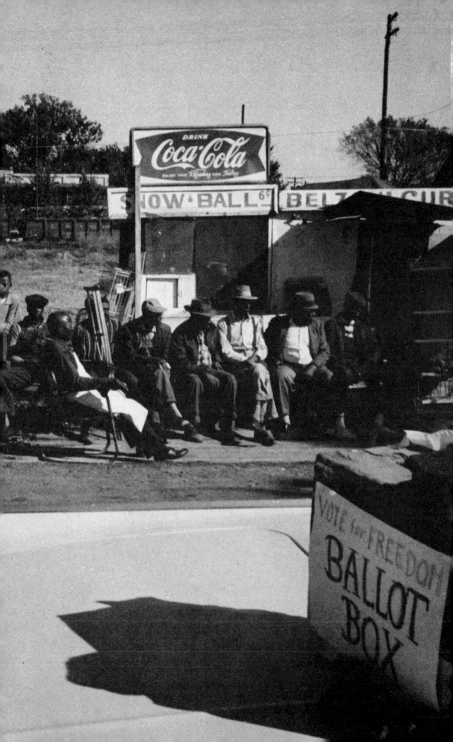

THIS THING WE CALL a Movement: what is it? It's not a revolution although journalists and TV commentators call it so. And Negro writers often call it so: the Negro Revolution, they say. But it is not a revolution; it is not a renaissance, either, nor an awakening although there have been rebirths and many who have been asleep are now wide awake. Malraux in speaking of periods of art likes to speak of resuscitations but this movement is not that, either. It is none of these but it has aspects of all of them in it. Maybe it is good that we are not pinned to an ideology: you get enslaved to it, it becomes your theology.

Labels seem irrelevant to me because what we are involved in is life itself: we are asking for more life as human beings; we are asking for freedom to breathe as men, to grow as children.

At night, after working all day down here in Mississippi, I push it out and try to find the meaning of it all: how will it look a thousand years from now? I've read and reread *The Phenomenon of Man* by Teilhard du Chardin. What a book! Maybe the greatest of our times: this thing he calls noogenesis (not a word I like), this culture of man's that for 50,000 years, maybe 100,000, maybe much longer, has been forming a new atmosphere above the earth: a new thing that God has let man create, and that is re-creating the men who have created it. Human culture: beyond nature. Something God is working out with man. And it has just begun. We must think in large spans of time to understand the human condition. This is exciting to me.

Maybe, in a way, I am one of the monks of the Movement—a scholar who spends his day in a cotton patch but keeps his mind cloistered with philosophers and poets at night. Maybe. I smile at myself.

I'm a northern Negro; my ancestors were free and always lived in the North. I went to one of the Big Three Eastern colleges. I got into the movement after Montgomery, after those four college kids sat in, in Greensboro. After seeing it on TV I felt out of life, too immersed in books and ideas.

I came South, I picketed, I sat in, I worked with the Student Nonviolent Coordinating Committee. As did others, I went to jail. Stayed there several weeks. Everywhere I've been I've listened to white and black southerners talk. It is a curious thing: their voices are so much alike, soft, easy; and they have a special kind of humor which both respond to easily. I was startled. It got me down, a little. I began to feel like an Outsider to both. Not because I happen to have a Ph.D. Plenty southern whites and Negroes have Ph.D.'s. It was something Big they seemed to share with each other and I felt excluded.

66

Others did too (white and Negro from the North) and it made some of them peculiarly critical of the southern whites they met; they seemed almost jealous; feelings can certainly get mixed up.

It stayed on my mind. One day, a young southern Negro came into the room, with five baked sweet potatoes and a bag of boiled pinders—and what do you think? some fried chitterlings. I shied off from the chitlins (as they call them) and made for the boiled pinders. I called them boiled peanuts and the others laughed. I ate two to be polite. Southerners, black and white, ate them all quickly and with relish, then ate the chitlings along with the sweet potatoes. I manfully pushed down one piece of cold sweet potato. Couldn't make the chitlins. They laughed tolerantly. That tolerance set me apart. I felt segregated.

Memories . . . that's it. I had been asleep, had awakened and lying there in the dark I thought this: *memories*. Those southerners are tied and tangled in a web of common memories they can't escape and don't want to escape. Memories of food eaten in childhood . . . hot sand on bare feet (when I was a kid I walked on hot asphalt, and not barefoot if I could help it), moss they played on, sandspurs, cane grindings (there's something they call 'pole cat' a kind of scum that rises on the cane syrup while it is boiling), fishing in ponds; so much; even common hurts; each hurt in a different way by that old barbed wire of segregation but both hurt. And they know it. I felt this; it seemed to me they had something very wonderful that could take them through the hell of

this fight for rights, if they only held on to it. But at times, these southerners (black and white) would suddenly turn against each other, there'd be an awful flare-up, and the Negroes would say, "What the hell are these b—— whites doing in our movement!" And the whites, if they were girls, would suddenly get weepy and talk about collective guilt (either that they did or didn't believe in it) and they'd say they couldn't bear the burden of hate that Eastland and Russell, and the police and the southern governors had aroused and yet their friends in the Movement were asking this of them. This impossible thing! Then as suddenly, it would quiet down. After a little, somebody would pick up a guitar and they'd all sing and friendliness, and the knowledge of the terrible need around them, would creep back and soften everybody's edges. And there'd be, for a moment, something beautiful there: radiant and profound.

But these surges of hate and guilt are treacherous things; maybe the southern students' worst enemies. To fight for your civil rights "for everybody's, ours too" (as the white southerners say) to fight and get them—and then to find yourself hating each other, hating whites and whites hating you, afterward, that is a nice twentieth century hell for us to look forward to. And we're likely to land just there. But the good memories can save the southerners, at least— that is, if only they hold on to them by realizing how precious they are.

But what can white and Negro northerners share, what memories of a common childhood do they have?

Can they find enough, strong enough, sweet enough to save them, too? I don't know.

Rights—oh, God, if they weren't so necessary! But they are. And to get them the old System has to be broken down. In this respect we *are* engaged in a revolution, we are revolting against the system of White Supremacy—which is not democracy, even if Governors Wallace and Barnett claim they're one and the same. Can we keep the distinction? I sometimes wonder. Can we hold on to the necessity for good relationships? After the rights are gained, are we still going to remember that rights are nothing except an open path to good human relationships? I am not sure.

This is one reason why I left the sit-ins and picketings and public acts for a quieter way of working. I want to be sure we are going to have those good relationships; and I know we can't—we can't have any of the real things civil rights can open the door to— unless we as a people get our basic needs fulfilled first, or simultaneously with the other. Until we iron out our unequal status.

So: I'm here in Mississippi, working on the awesome needs of these people: the need to read and write, the need to learn how to register and vote, how to become informed enough to vote wisely; how to get training for a good job, how to maintain decent health, how to work for a decent living. All this. Mudsill stuff.

Those in the Movement are so few and the needs so great that it is like spooning up the Atlantic Ocean.

But maybe our efforts will draw attention to the depth and width of these needs; if this happens, surely the Federal government will help with its poverty program, despite the efforts of Mississippi and other southern Congressmen to keep it from helping. But at night, it bears down hard on you. This is why, after staring across the fields of the Delta, after having struggled for two hours by lamp light to teach fifteen men and women to write their name and read directions, I turn away to the *Phenomenon of Man*—to get a little perspective on the human condition—and a little needed distance.

In the daytime, I concentrate on the small smudgy problems that arise and I see things this way: The glaring inequalities of Negroes are matched only by the glaring inequalities of many poor whites—down here in the Delta as well as in the hill country of Appalachia. That is why, when we work to help Negroes, we've got to be willing to work to help the poor whites: people so poor, so deprived of hope and inner dignity that they've not even learned yet to protest. We cannot forget those mudsill whites: it won't do for us to forget. For everything gets out of balance when we do. Not even Negroes suffer as do some of the migrant whites. There are Negro migrants, too; it is hard to balance the books and say which suffers more, the poor Negro or the poor white.

So, here I am: trying to ease out the inequalities so that Negroes may rise to a level where good relationships are possible; so that poor whites may rise to a level where good relationships are possible.

In a sense I am an "alien," a "foreign missionary." Why don't I work up North? That question would require an autobiography for an answer. Let me say this: the South appeals to me; its poignant needs appeal to something deep in me; Harlem has even worse needs, South Side in Chicago does, all the northern ghettos; but this appeals to me—and one must work where one's heart and intuition send one. And too, my reason tells me the core of the trouble is in the South, its malignant center is here and we must cure it at its center before we can rid the North of its infection.

I don't think this kind of work is more urgent than to fight segregation. Both are necessary. We must learn to see not either-or but both; for in life it is always both. I certainly don't think everybody should come off the streets as many whites beg us to do. But we've got not only to see the "both," we've got to think on three big levels at one time and this is not easy for activists to do. So, maybe, the Movement can take a few "monks," a few poets and scholars of both races who are aware of where demogoguery with its half-truths and exaggerations leads the masses and knowing this, who try to inject a bit of wisdom and perspective into these wild, tumultuous affairs. The short view, the long view, the double view are necessary.

This keeps occurring to me: remembering the poor whites and the ways in which they've been cheated in the South for 150 years, how can we then want only Negroes to have Very Special Treatment? We

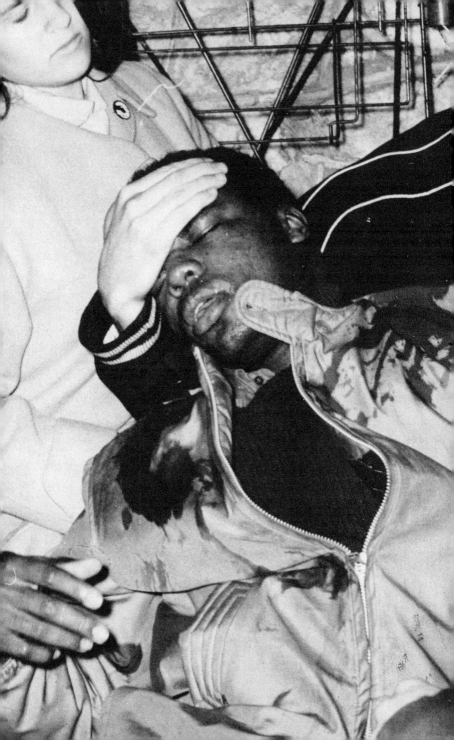

want all the poor, the ignorant, the sick, the shamed, the homeless and the out-of-work of both races to have Very Special Treatment. We must hold on to this; it is as important as for southerners to hold on to their sweet, sad, poignant, terrible memories.

Nonviolence? Deep in my heart I wonder

THE JET WAS LIFTING, water was under us, New Orleans was behind us, everything terrible behind us, we were leaving what your mind can't work out, your soul—

No. Not leaving it. It was just dropping farther away below us. Distance was segregating it, making it small enough to say for a second, It's gone!

But it is here. Always here inside me. Always here inside every one of us in this country. You can't shut yourself away from terror and hate any more than you can from fall-out. The blast *is:* it has happened. Feelings have exploded and the fall-out is just beginning.

I stared below me: so green, spring here, summer almost here, water gone now, soft green life growing everywhere, so beautiful, so scary as it bursts through death. And here we are, we Negroes, we whites, fertilizing the greenness with hate and fear. What is wrong? What is WRONG WITH US? Down in the Delta, there we were: most of us young, some of us Negro, a few white: human beings on a mission to help other human beings, and sometimes we behaved like devils! Why? Spilling over with honest ideals, absolutely willing to die for dignity and freedom, for the poor little poked-out bellied children—and turning on each other, storming out at each other: *Why don't you m—— f—— whites go home! Why do you stay? we don't want you we can do more without you—* And a voice that was humbly disturbed last night about a family in desperate need, saying in a cool proud white voice, *Why do you hate us so?*

Oh God! Why do you hate us so? Us us us us! YOU'RE IN OUR WAY, a black guy said. YOU CLUTTER UP OUR MINDS, YOU DRAG UP THE PAST YOUR PRESENCE KEEPS REMINDING US OF HOW YOU ALWAYS COME OUT ON TOP.

ON TOP OF WHAT? cool white voice trembling now; the girls always cry, they can't take it without showing they're hurt.

"ON TOP OF THE HEAP. SEE? Don't you remember?" black voice urgent with sarcasm, "don't you remember history?"

And sometimes a white voice will say, after swallowing hard, "I understand; I know white skin is something it's easy to react to; like Pavlov's dog and the bell, etc. But this is pure physical reaction, pure behaviorism—and we should be *responding*, not reacting. The Klan reacts to your black skin, too; but you're not on the level of Klansmen, are you? I don't understand why you load us with the sins of millions of whites who are indifferent when *we care*. We honestly care!"

And then a soft black voice says, "We know, we know you care but we're jealous, maybe, for fear you'll be a little smarter somehow, show us up, some-how."

"You can't mean that. You're a Ph.D. I haven't even finished college. If I ever question anything you do it's when my experience as a white warns me of white psychology. I don't think you always under-stand white psychology; you fear it, hate it but you don't always understand it—although maybe your old grandfather did."

"Damn! Don't you see? That's what you always do! Talking about dear old Uncle Tom grandfather whose wisdom—"

"But you are stereotyping. And stereotyping is a big sin, no matter who does it. If your grandfather understood the twisting of a white man's mind it was because he had to deal with it successfully in order to stay alive. It wasn't because he was an Uncle Tom!"

On and on and on, like this. Oh, this would please Senator Eastland and Governor Wallace. This is ex-actly the way they hope we will behave with each other. But we're under strain—more maybe than the GI's in combat; a more subtle strain. We never know what's going to happen next; the incidents we get involved in pierce us to the bone; we have no built-in resistance to this kind of strain. We want to be in-dividuals but everything is organized around the idea of color blocs. Everything! And the whites in the Delta are pretty awful; the indifference of the nice ones is harder to take than the cruelty and ob-scenity of the cops and politicians and racists. Add

to it things happening everywhere else; add to it the stunning coldheartedness of those southern senators in Congress whose stall-in is far worse, many times worse than the stall-in that didn't happen at the World's Fair. But who criticizes those senators? There is no nation-wide criticism; just a few liberals, a few church people speak up against them. But when we Negroes do something—oh my! the high moral standard expected of us. And we try; God, how we try to keep cool, to feel compassion, to stay nonviolent—but how *can* you with pressure after pressure after pressure! And so, to keep from taking guns and shooting things out in the Delta we turn against these white kids helping us down here. Sure, we know it's not easy for them to come and help. But *nothing is easy for us. Nothing!* So we turn on them and we storm and we curse and we—well, we take it out on them in a pretty rough way. And we hate them, really hate them, sometimes; and we don't understand these feelings in us, we are ashamed, we don't justify, we know we can't—and yet—

You need to be a saint to stay nonviolent in the Delta. You're ringed with violence, internal and external; it's everywhere. How you going to meet this violence with the ordinary love and compassion of an ordinary man or woman? It just can't be done. OK. I'm glad I said it: It just can't be done.

So what do you do next? Is there something between nonviolence and violence that will work? What? Gandhi with his talk of love and search for truth somehow kept the rage of the Indians from spilling over on the British; but when India got its freedom, this pent-up rage spilled out, rose like a tidal wave against fellow Indians: Hindus against Muslims, Muslims against Hindus; all of them fellow-Indians but suddenly they were raping, killing each other, burning houses; and finally, to finish it off a fellow-Hindu assassinated Gandhi—as if to say, "You made us better than we were able to be; you told us we could love instead of hate; well, we can't, see?" And so he shot the Mahatma in the garden at prayer meeting. I wonder, sometimes, if we who believe in nonviolence have correctly analyzed that situation in India: its psychological and philosophical roots? Have we ever admitted that the Indians turned a kind of double rage on fellow Indians—all they hadn't turned on the British? Have we admitted that nonviolence didn't work, after all?

Or did it? I don't know. It worked; and it didn't work.

I looked below; we were getting close to a city; we were not coming down; I wasn't sure where we were. From the Delta, from thousands of acres of black land and little shanties I had now come back to—the city. And this meant for me, the ghetto. I was born in Harlem. Not in a ghetto area—unless it is all that. I lived on one of the better streets; but I was born and brought up with the smells and sights and sounds of the ghetto around me. City ghetto, rural ghetto. Which is worse? The climate is easier on you in Mississippi, and the tempo of living is easier. But poverty is the same, and lack of hope. The speed in a city

ghetto, yes . . . that is worse—for you have less time
to think, to dream, to pray about things. A killing is
a killing, anywhere, I guess; but to me, a city woman,
a killing in the Delta seems worse; no reason for this,
it just seems worse, maybe because you have more
time to think about it, what happpened, why it happened, who did it—all that.

I wanted to leave the Delta, felt I couldn't take any
more of it—at least, for a while; but I dread getting
back to New York, to Harlem, to *our* pattern of rage,
our pattern of loneliness, *our* pattern of sin, *our* pattern of stereotyping. Harlem and the Delta—which
is worse, which is better? God only knows. But the
tempo makes it harder in Harlem: harder to know
people as people, harder to think something out,
harder to be alone, although you're just as lonely as
in the Delta. Harder to form a relationship. We say
we are fighting for our civil rights—but *why* are we?
Unless it is to be free to form real relationships with
our world. But even with civil rights, it is hard in a
rushing city to form a real relationship with anything
—a person or a book or an experience. And here is
the real meaning of nonviolence: the reality or the
truth of a relationship. Everything in your life is
violent except the parts of it that are true and real; a
lie is violence, a half lie is violence; telling a half lie
about "white people" or about "black people" is as
violent as knocking somebody down. That is why it
is so hard to practice nonviolence; because it is hard
to reject all that is not true and real. We've got to
think nonviolently if we want to think the truth. The

85

truth of me—do I dare think it? The truth of my affair, my relationship with M.—do I dare know that truth? If I don't, then I am practicing violence. Every time I stereotype anybody, or any group or any situation I am thinking violently. Every time I evade seeing this whole civil rights-segregation-human-relations Thing as it is, every time I look at it on the surface, refusing an understanding of its depths and heights, I am committing a spiritual violence.

So—if we learn a little, even a little (as did the Indians) about the meaning of nonviolence, maybe it will be worth our failures. Maybe we've got to become extraordinary people in order to do nonviolently what must be done in this world. We talk about peace . . . maybe we have not confessed that as persons we may not, yet, be capable of achieving peace, because we are not, as yet, capable of achieving a nonviolent life of the mind, the spirit, the psyche.

But we can't stop trying. Even if we fail, we won't fail entirely; surely this is right. Trouble with us down in the Delta working at our "mission," we thought we could do it, succeed at it, and still remain nice, "normal," ordinary people. Well, we can't. This is our ordeal: out of it we'll come all wizened up, or bigger, stronger, maybe extraordinary. In a sense, to reach for excellence is more thrilling than to reach for "equality." Maybe, to get equality of opportunity for the masses (white and Negro) some of us have got to grow until we ache and pain all over.

Negroes (and the whites who help us) thought we

were undertaking a more or less "natural" thing when we started this revolution for our rights; but if we succeed, we will have to do more than we dreamed of in the beginning. Maybe this is why some whites get so upset and keep asking, "But what else are they going to want?" Maybe like two fighting dogs we have one end of the truth in our teeth and they have another end in theirs. Maybe deepdown they are fearing not "intermarriage" as they say but the fact that to achieve the right kind of human relations we've got to change as people—all of us, Negro and white; maybe they sense it, that they've got to find a little excellence, too; that we all have got to throw away "superior" and substitute for it "extraordinary."

They say we're nearing Newark Airport. Well, I'm back—back to a keyed-up people, lonely and lost, like me; not at all sure what is right but shouting that they are sure; back to white people as indifferent, as blind, some of them, as the people in Jackson. I'm going to stay up here. I think I "belong" here and should work here where I know our ways and customs; it is better than being a missionary in Mississippi; and yet, I'm not sure; it'll be easier, up here, to forget, to grow absorbed in my own affairs. Who had any personal affairs in our group in the Delta? That is one reason it was so exciting: we were a Corps doing something very special; oh, we fussed at each other, we sometimes raged, but we loved each other too; even now, having been away for a few hours, I begin to wonder why I let S. and T. get on my nerves; their southern accent had begun to

send me wild. Now, even now, I wonder why. I sus-
pect my Harlem accent upset them, too. It won't be
as adventurous at home—but just as hard; things are
tough here. Hold on; don't chicken. You've got a job
to do. Wonder what they're having for supper, down
there? Hot dogs and a can of baked beans, unless a
family asked them to eat turnip greens with them.
Such sweet hospitality: "We've got a mess of turnip
greens, come home and eat with us."

Mama, I got to do it,
  I got to

MAMA was talking. She was crying, too, and I couldn't make out some of her words, but I knew what she meant. "But you'll git killed, this place is different, Mississippi is different, you can't do it. I got along, why can't you just get along, son, like your old ma and pa? There's a way to make out, you got to learn it, boy, this way they'll kill you. All my life I worked to make it easier for you and now you want to tear it all up, you can't do nothing to change white folks, you just can't, I know, you're young but I know, all you can do is pray and try to git along." She hid her face in her apron. It wasn't easy but I had to say it, I had to.

Mama, I told her, this is something I can do. All my life down here I didn't know nothing to do; now I got something I can do. I'm going to help the others, I got to. Mama said, "What can you do, boy? What? There's nothing you can do to change white folks, you can't, no more'n you can stop the old river, you can't."

I got to, Mama, I told her. I'm going to help register our people so they can vote. Don't say anything, Mama, I got to do it; don't try to stop me. I may get in jail, I may get killed, but the time's come, Mama,

93

we can't keep on like this. We got to show everybody that we are people, we want to vote, we're Americans, Mama, and we got to show everybody that we are. We got to wake folks up, they dead asleep, they give up too easy, we got to say, 'Stop giving up, stop it! Register and vote; you may git killed trying but try, you gotta try!' Everybody's gotta try, Mama, to show they not dogs and cows but people; they got to look white folks in the eye, got to be polite and law-abiding, but they got to look up, Mama, not down at the dirt, no more. We got to. Uncle Rob was killed in the last war, and you got his medal and you've been real proud. Well, I may die, Mama, and if I do I hope you'll be proud, too, not all broke up, Mama, but proud that I did what an American ought to do, work for his people's rights as citizens.

And Mama cried under her apron and said, "And all these years I worked my hands to the bone hoping to make things better for you and now, you go and git yourself in jail or maybe killed, I ask Jesus, Why? What have I done wrong that my boy wants to git himself jailed by breaking laws and sassing white folks and—"

Mama, I told her, please mam, listen to me. I don't want to be a nigger, I want to be a Negro American, I want us all to have our rights and to get our rights we got to stand up for em, we got to, Mama. I know white folks, I know old Sheriff M— I know he would shoot a nigger down easy as a pole cat; but I got to help change things, we got to make white folks *think*, Mama, think, and understand that we're real people, too. I'm goin be polite, but I'm goin to look in their faces, no more down at the dirt. Mama, you ask Jesus —you pray and ask Jesus if I ain't right; I think he'll say, "Yes, he's right, he's got to do this, he's got to help change a hating Mississippi into a loving one." I think He'll say it, Mama, but you ask Him.

And I left her crying real soft behind her apron. Poor old Mama, she can't see it any plainer than some of the white folks that the world has changed, and we got to change, too. Oh God, help Mama see it so she won't be too hurt, help her; and help the rest of us, if You can, help us, too, a little.

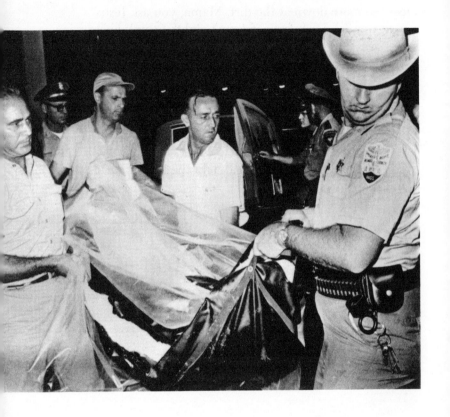

**You think about the three
who were killed**

You think about the three who were killed, you think about the six or seven Negroes whose names nobody quite remembers who were killed earlier, and the dozens who were beaten and maimed, and the hundreds of young Civil Rights workers who, brave and scared, unarmed except with compassion and belief in human dignity and their yearning for freedom, are risking their lives every day hoping to help, hoping somehow to dramatize human need so their fellow Americans cannot turn away and forget, you think of this: and then you think of the mobs, of the bands of psychotic terrorists, of the "poor whites," not poor any more in terms of money, but poor and deprived in terms of human culture, of spiritual richness, of civilized morality. The poor whites—how terrible they are! How afraid everybody is to see this cultural depletion. Look at their faces in the mobs, look at the policemen's faces, look at the sheriffs and their deputies with criminal records; study those faces hard, look deep into the emptiness of their souls and then remember who made them that way: the old planter, yes, even now trying to do the same in rural areas, but the early industrialist, too, the early factory owners of the South who made their workers sharecroppers just as surely as the farm workers were sharecroppers—taking everything away from these whites except the drug of white superiority. The powerful ones fed the poor whites this drug so they wouldn't crave the bread their bodies needed and the values their souls had to have. And now, they collect in mobs with their guns and their iron bars and they are protected by the cops with their tear gas and cattle prods, and most of us try to see only little bits of what is happening, try not to recognize its significance for us.

And I get up on Sunday in my pulpit and try to say the truth. I look down on those glazed, smooth faces of the indifferent ones, and my heart sickens. Something tells me to go easy, be tactful, be gentle, and something else in me that I think is closer to Jesus Christ tells me to drive these indifferent ones, these dead souls out of His temple. And I think, how can I do it? How does one, today, drive the indifferent ones out of the holy places and tell them to stay away until they have cleansed their souls and done something, acted, spoken to change this terrible Thing that has come so close to destroying us at the center of our being?

Yes, this is part of the Movement, too: the movement toward a clean, honest, compassionate life for all men, the movement of our century toward relationships that are deep and real, the movement toward quality, excellence. I feel part of this Movement. Yet I have never demonstrated on the streets. And this troubles me: perhaps things have gone so far that every decent person must demonstrate in a public place, maybe in church, maybe in a business club, maybe on the streets to push away this Thing, this Terrible Thing that has come too close to us: this spiritual indifference, this "I don't really care," this "Why did they go to Mississippi unless they were looking for trouble?," this awful non-involvement that has turned some of our towns and cities over to the "poor white" mobs and their demagogues, to these pitiful creatures who get their kicks out of looking down on Negroes, who in their addiction cling to segregation as the only thing that makes life endurable for them.

I am torn by this. I cannot get it off my mind. I think one day I should stay in my church, try to help these indifferent ones find their way to compassion and concern; and then I think, No! I, too, should go to Mississippi and risk my life with these young ones who are doing something that most Americans think will not help. But how can we say that? Jesus and his Twelve were a pitiful little group: nobody in our twentieth century, today, would think a group like that could change anything. But THEY did. How do we know these young demonstrators cannot with God's help bring miracles to pass? We don't know. And it is this loss of faith, this compulsive dependence upon numbers, quantity instead of quality, that is pushing us away from personal integrity and the spiritual power that comes to us when we do what is right.

My congregation, except for twelve or twenty, maybe, do not believe this. They use God's church for social purposes, to give them status and a spurious security. Oh, they have their charities but little that touches them. Then why do I stay in the church? Why? I ask myself—and the answer is hard to find. I think I still believe God can work miracles even in the church; but I don't know: God, as we look at human history, has had a way of choosing one man, one boy, one woman or a small band of men to do His work. The church should sustain the work that the lonely ones do—that is its job—but does it?

I envy those in the Movement who have practical ways of helping, such as the Skills Banks to help Negroes find jobs they are fitted for; I envy those who are working on better housing in the cities; I know these earthy, practical things must be done and more and more of them. But I also know that my job may be simply to risk and maybe die to help Negroes find their way out of the swamps that White Supremacy put them in; I know that I may need to do this, that some of us whites may need to die for our collective sins. I know this. And I sit here thinking of the Three, wondering what helped them through it at the last, wondering what they thought about, hoping they believed their deaths would not be wasted. And we must not waste these deaths. Nor can we waste the deaths of the unknown Negroes killed in Mississippi and other rural parts of the South week after week, often without any news of the deaths getting to the cities. And we cannot waste their deaths by forgetting the poor whites who are in many ways far more caught in human misery, in spiritual emptiness than are most Negroes. A hater is a dehumanized man; how can we do else but pity these wounded creatures and try to bring them back into human society which the powerful ones of our fathers' time pushed them out of.

I have no answers right now: just hurting questions, just an aching mind, a torn spirit. All I can pray for is that we not waste the sacrifices of the young and brave, that we tear our indifference from us so that we, too, can be free. Will America hear in time? Are we headed toward a lawless time of mobs and ghosts and brutality of hand and spirit? Are we? I fear it and yet something in me cries No! We'll find the right road. We must. We'll somehow find the new faith, the courage, the energy that will help us change. I pray so.

The day it happens

For some it happened yesterday. For some it is beginning today. For a few it happened years ago. Eyes turn, and are looking in a new direction. Ears pick up a sentence never understood before. A child moves across one's imagination, a crash startles one's soul, a whisper shakes the memory.

In such small ways comes the big change.

The movement of whites and Negroes toward a new future has its beginning for each of us without help of calendar. "Except for the still point, there would be no dance." There is a waiting; a long waiting for some; a waiting without end for those who cannot meet the new life. For those who can, there comes their moment in time—and a new beginning.

For Joseph A. McNeil, David Richmond, Ezell A. Blair, Jr., and Franklin E. McClain it began when they sat-in at a white restaurant in Greensboro, N. C., in 1960, and somehow startled the whole world by their act. For Martin Luther King it began in Montgomery, Alabama, one night in 1955. For Mrs. Rosa Parks, the moment came a few days earlier in the same city, as she sat in a bus, tired from a day's work: she was asked to move back, and suddenly her entire life came together, fused in one terrific moment of decision, and she said "No." That word "No," which she had not planned to say, did not know she was about to say, changed the tempo of racial change for our entire nation.

For others, the new movement began in their childhood, building itself out of minute hurts, insights, dreams, hopes, until somehow a new design was created and a new way of living began. It must have started in the first decade of this century for Walter White, who saw the act of lynching as a metaphor of dehumanization for his entire race and committed his life to finding a new way for his people. For that doughty old warrior, Philip Randolph, his moment came when he first entered the labor movement, for always he saw the shadow of race haunting its struggles; for Jim Farmer, for Roy Wilkins, for Anna Hedgman, for Bayard Rustin, for Constance Baker Motley, for numerous other Negroes and whites, one turns back to the late '30's and '40's for the moment they said No to the old way.

Perhaps it does not matter when and how the Movement started: perhaps it began too long ago to find a certainty of date, too long to know just who spoke out when, and how. But as Negroes, one by one, and ten by ten and finally hundreds by thousands stood up and cried, No! to the old pressures of white supremacy, a few hundred white southerners also said No! And a few hundred white northerners also said No! And then, more and more. Many a struggle, many a shrewd act, many a quiet talk with "the

Powers" had taken place, many new patterns of non-violent protests had been formed long before the Montgomery protest, long before Little Rock, long before the famous Supreme Court decision of 1954. Books that shook the world had been written long before; there had even been one sudden, large-sized grass-roots protest in the South made against segregation by both Negroes and whites, in 1938, in 1940, in 1942; earlier, southern churchwomen had protested lynching in persistent and dramatic ways.

Teilhard du Chardin has said so rightly that the beginnings of all change on this earth are lost in a creative dimness; there is surely no need here to do more than remind those who wonder why it began to happen in 1960 that it actually did not begin to happen then. Never, since the Civil War, has protest ceased entirely; it was almost crushed, almost smothered, again and again, but never completely so: always it took another breath, kept breathing—and through the decades because of two World Wars, because of at least five mind-shaking books, because of many test cases carried to the Supreme Court by the NAACP, because of individuals (Negro and white) who spoke out bravely and beautifully, because of studies made on all aspects of this thing we call "race," insights spread, illuminations touched minds, and we as a people acquired a new sensitiveness to our failures and inadequacies. Perhaps more than all else, was the effect television had on us in our homes and on the news gatherers; where once newspapers had played down incidents, smothered stories that should have been told, television met the challenge with startling directness and forced newspapers to tell things as they are. (Not that all newspapers even now do, but there has been, during the past ten years, a tremendous change.) The awakening of Africa and Asia to the political potentials had its effect, also.

Perhaps we should say this: by 1960 the flood of protests, the powerful words spoken or written by a few poets and novelists, the decisions of the courts, the world political currents, and the acts of protest, added up to a kind of awesome Orphic truth which once heard transforms the hearer into something better—or worse.

The mind of America shuddered, trembled—and changed. How could any but morons and mad men be the same after the dynamiting of those four little girls at Sunday School in Birmingham? how could complacency remain uncracked after seeing on TV the courage of the nine students in the Little Rock high school? How could any heart bear the weight of the cowardly killing of Medgar Evers? of the killing of growth in children everywhere? Even domestic animals feel shame: surely most Americans must have felt shame at watching the Oxford affair, and before that, the wanton behavior of women in front of schools in New Orleans. There are images that can never be forgotten, sounds that echo through a lifetime: bind these with the searching truth of a few who have written and spoken and acted—and the past becomes a catalyst which the future cannot escape the effect of.

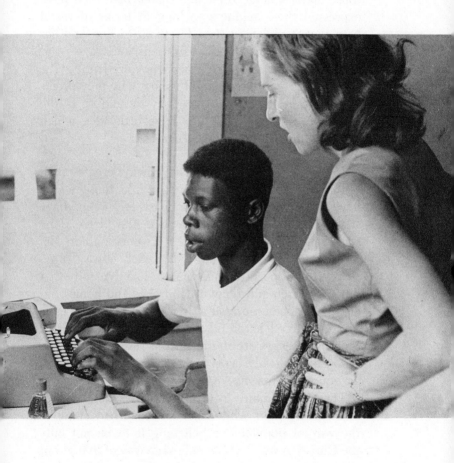

The future is, to a large extent, already shaping up. The greedy politician will not admit it; the morons cannot change their minds; the mad men have expressed their madness so long in terms of racial hate that it will take time for them to find another way of living out their frustrations and rage. And always the ones who profit in money are stubbornly, stupidly slow. Profiteers rarely know why they profit; because they don't know, they try to hold on to the entire *status quo,* since they have little idea which part of it has actually profited them.

CRISES ARE TWO-EDGED; they always create possibilities for both evil and good. While those which have piled on us during the past few years have shaken many white people awake, they have done something different to Negroes. Twenty million Negroes have been wounded by each crisis, often stripped of hope, often humiliated. The dynamite that killed children and blew up churches and homes has also blown open repressions in minds and hearts: each blast has freed hate and resentment in hundreds of thousands; every stubborn form of resistance of governors and officials, every police brutality has aroused an equal stubbornness in the protesters.

There were many Negroes who had found a way of forgiving their white enemies; they had clung to the way of nonviolence believing it to be not only the Christian way but the only sane way of living; but every nasty speech of a politician, every police dog, every fire hose and cattle prod used on black human beings, has lessened their love, their faith—and their prayers have grown shorter. How long, O Lord, how long can they endure such pressures!

Their leaders are beginning to ask themselves: can nonviolence work in our American society? can it work unless it is understood? can it be understood if white people harden their hearts and turn away? The leaders are also asking, How can we convince the young Negroes that this is the right way, the only creative way to work? how can we persuade them of the need of dialogue when fire hose and cattle prods are turned on them? The students' calmness, their patience, their self-control under the vicious circumstances they confront has been amazing. But how long can it last? How long can they endure the pompous scolding of white editorials when U.S. senators say what they say, and the "big mules" do what they do, and are only mildly rebuked by a few editors and often not rebuked at all.

It is more than access to public accommodations that the Negroes and their white friends want but this access must be won first so the people can be as free as are other citizens. It may well be that voting is more important, in that voting brings power; but to move freely in public places brings grace to one's life. It may be more sensible to go after better jobs and better job training, but being human, one still longs more for freedom to be at ease in one's hometown.

BUT THERE IS something beyond rights, something not more important but more desperately urgent: bodily need. There are millions of Negroes in such desperate need in town and country and city that talk of "rights" leaves them dull and dazed. The young protesters who come, in large part, from middle-class families have stumbled on this: to their stunned amazement they have found a primitive misery which pushes the phrase "civil rights" out of their vocabulary.

They have found in Mississippi, Alabama, Louisiana, other states, too, and in cities, North and South, pockets of raw deprivation where all a human craves is a piece of bread, a coat, a shelter. The economic problem in these places is often not "low wages" but no money at all. Many cannot read or write even their name. There are no books, few schools worthy of the name. This is zero land. In the Delta, it acquires a nightmare edge of absurdity for soil is rich, rainfall favorable, climate pleasant: nature has been good to people—all that is wrong is the White Supremacy system and those who run it. The Federal government is willing to give aid to these sufferers in the usual way of surplus foods and aid to children under state welfare departments but the white powers of certain Delta counties often will not let Negroes accept this aid.

In the city ghettos, as in New York, it is almost worse: a wolf-like misery has gnawed at an entire family until the little children act as though their tongues were bitten off. Some of them have lost or never acquired the ability to speak. They look at you mutely, they cannot make a sentence. They need not their "rights" but love—a human necessity some have not experienced; and without a little love, without a little care, the human child sometimes cannot learn even to say words.

Realizing this, many in the Student Nonviolent Coordinating Committee, in CORE, in the NAACP are now turning their energies in new directions. "Civil rights" is the name of one destination that must be arrived at quickly, for the sake of the nation's spiritual equilibrium; but hidden away, in the rural places, in alleys, on back streets in open and closed cities and towns there are these giant needs that will not be put off.

To meet them, to help people want to learn, want to work, want to live, one must work out a very real relationship with them; it is not enough to give them hand-outs of food, things, books; one must give concern, understanding—this is the only bridge these tremulous, quietly raging people can walk across. The students in the Movement are learning this.

Here is the point of change: where systems are abandoned and human relationships are begun. Thank God, there are some places in the North but also in the South, where bridges can even now be built, where walls are low enough to climb over. One exciting expression of this new realization of the need to relate is that of the college students' tutorial committees. Many students are giving hours of their time to tutoring the Negro pupils who need help; some

work with the drop-outs to help them gain the confidence to go back and try again.

How did this start? No one quite knows. One day, an imagination stirred, energies awakened, a problem was confronted, a mind saw a way to help; others, hearing about it, responded. Each student has his day when it happens to him: *here is something I can do that is worth doing.*

The Movement is by no means limited to sit-ins, picket lines, parades of protest. The March to Washington was an important gesture of spiritual depth and one participated in by most of the serious groups of nonviolent protesters. Hundreds of smaller symbolic protests have been made. But the Movement is much more than what happens in public places. There have been (and are) the legal battles in courtrooms that moved things but oh, so slowly until the sit-ins, acting as enzymes, began to accelerate the consequences. There is the organized search for jobs and training to prepare for jobs. There is the housing problem and its syndrome of social ills and much is being done about it by the Urban League. There are the quiet tutorial personal relationships now being developed by the thousands; there are the voter registration campaign and the programs of adult education.

Above all else, the Movement is in no sense a revolution against our political system. It opposes the extra-legal, subversive system of White Supremacy with its mobs and its ghosts and its rituals and its Witches' Sabbath murders and its web of spies and censorship, and police pressures. It opposes all this, yes; but it has no rival system to set up in its place. The Movement thinks of itself as a valid expression of the democratic way; and its leaders remember that democracy is not a system, that it has no ideology; it is a way of life, a *Tao*, a continuous series of specific attempts to protect every individual's freedom to grow, to ask questions, to work, to explore inner and outer space, to create the New Thing and the New Relationship.

We are on trembling earth now: ground that is sensitive to the slightest pressure; a place where the weight of authority and force does not belong. For we are trying to substitute relationships, each with its inner dynamics, its specific pulls and strains, and its easements, for a rigid system. No wonder both Negroes and whites are confused!

To be half animal, half automaton and live under a regime that makes the decisions is so much easier than accepting one's own responsibilities. Many Negroes, today, are only too willing to slip out of one slave system straight into another, as the popularity of Black Nationalism suggests. Black Nationalism offers no follower his freedom; it offers him a flight from freedom, a new form of slavery—this time, slavery to hatred of whites and to black arrogance.

Perhaps one can explain the Sahara-minds of many white segregationists as another consequence of the System. There are the U. S. Senators from the South who seem to know only one crude human relationship called "sex." The struggle for human rights, com-

plex and deeprooted, brings only one question to their minds: *Would you want your sister to marry, etc.?* How tiresome and empty! How hideously absurd! But this is the way the System works: by tearing out nuances, differences, all the varieties and subtleties of the human experience, life is reduced to one sliver. Segregation has so dessicated minds that it is impossible for its adherents to conceive of a Negro's and white's ability to respond, to relate each to the other—or both to a Bartok Quartet, or to a William Golding novel, or to a painting or a poem or a winsome song, or to an errand of mercy; or to the reading and discussion, perhaps, of Teilhard du Chardin's *Phenomenon of Man;* or to watching a film of Bergman's, or enjoying a James Bond escapade, or talking politics, or maybe hoeing together a row of cabbage, or cooking hot dogs, or watching a fog come over East River. No; the tight old segregationists apparently cannot conceive of minds and souls responding one to another on various levels, and to the world around them; no, always and always and always, they snicker and ask, *Do you want your sister etc.*

Knowing this, how can we fail to acknowledge the awesome injuries which segregation has inflicted on every one of us! I cannot believe one American has escaped its effect. We only have to observe how crookedly, awkwardly our minds work in the entire field of human and personal relationships. Segregation is a potent idea for evil: it almost forces one to shun the truth; the word itself holds a witch doctor's holiness, a form of "holiness" which that interesting writer, Rudolph Otto,* speaks of as that "overplus" beyond the good, that portion of the numinous which is the antonym of God. Man is a broken creature who can never be solid: he is made whole only by his relationships: segregation is, therefore, his mortal enemy for it tears his relationships to pieces. No one ever segregated man or idea or dream without segregating his own life on many of its levels. For Malcolm X and his hate-filled followers to talk now of a new kind of segregation reveals the cruel stupidity that hate imposes on minds; their minds are now functioning on the same splintered level as Klansmen and white racial fanatics.

Feelings, thoughts, intuitive flashes such as these are running as a quiet current beneath the sounds and acts of the Movement. Will hate win by setting up new systems of bondage? Will love lose in its search for the real relationship that can grow? Do we yet realize that the quality of every person depends on how many real relationships he can create or respond to?

And now, these questions are exacerbated by the intruders in the Movement. Perhaps it could not have been otherwise in this world of good and evil. There was a purity of vision the Evil One was compelled to contaminate. The leaders and their early followers went into their nonviolent activities with a deep sense of commitment, with a cleanness of purpose, a longing to absorb through their suffering the wrongs

* *The Idea of the Holy.* Rudolph Otto.

of all our people. *Redemption* became for them a numinous word—for the more naïve, almost a magic word—certainly one they all hungered to understand. And there was a surge of joy, of adventure, yes; of courage—almost reckless courage, full of laughter. It was beautiful to see. Perhaps never in American history has there been a movement of such gayety and intellectual richness—the poetry some of the students chant (and write), the philosophy the leaders read, the theology young and old struggle through—Buber, Tillich, Bultman, Kierkegaard—all this done in their search for the good life which they hunger to substitute for the hollow thing-obsessed life too many of us have lived. And all of it streaked with a fine sense of humor and a humility they express in prayer—and an increasing closeness to "the people."

Then, slowly and more and more swiftly, came the Intruders: exploiting the amazing success many of the projects had had. For the sit-ins opened hundreds of restaurants, hundreds of hotels and motels, many parks; the picketing opened all the services of one big department store after another to Negroes; many stores began to hire Negroes even in the deep South; buses were integrated. These things were miracles. They happened and happened swiftly. Sympathetic city officials, editors, chambers of commerce often begged for a let-up; they even suggested that the Negroes would do better by getting off the streets and back into the courts. But Negroes and their white friends smiled at this: for it was only after public sit-ins and picketing and other forms of public protest that results were obtained. What the thoughtful whites had in mind, however, was not unreasonable: they wanted rest periods to give the next level of whites time to adjust to the new conditions; all whites are not equally intelligent, all are not equally informed; all are not equally balanced, emotionally; time is needed for many to bend physical and mental muscles in new ways. And perhaps we should remember that it takes time to recover from drug addiction; and many whites are addicted to White Supremacy: it has affected minds, emotions, values. The whole country is suffering from withdrawal pains.

Just at this sensitive moment, came the Intruders: North and South they began to make a dangerous caricature of the Nonviolent Movement: with diabolical cleverness they assumed the outer ways without making the inner sacrifices and spiritual decisions. There is nothing on earth more dangerous than a violent man pretending to be nonviolent—nothing more dangerous except ten or a hundred of them.

The work of the Intruders is the activity of hate disguised. This is what Denis de Rougemont calls, "the Devil's shrewd trick." Always the Devil appears in each age in the costumes of the Good and using their vocabulary. Here he is, with his hating, half-mad followers dressed up as nonviolent protesters, wreaking ruin as he goes, stirring the wrath even of the Negro group's most loyal friends, irritating every fair-minded Negro and white. Added to this serious situation is the not well controlled ambition of a few, a very few (let's remember) young leaders who are listening to the neo-nihilism of our times (a curious mixture of Genet, Sartre, Spengler and American Beats), and somehow blending this foamy stuff with their own personal ambition—with results that arouse even their friends' grave concern.

But let me say this plainly: these Intruders, and the few young leaders who have been seduced by quick success and their own lack of intellectual maturity, are no more dangerous, no more blind and not nearly so ruthless as the group of whites who cling to their Whiteness, who listen to their secret hate feelings and are quick to criticize every protest of Negroes, although they never seem to see the cruelties and greed of whites who control real estate and industry and certain unions, and who put the stealthy, unbearable pressures on urban Negroes.

We must take care that we see the picture whole: that we measure, also, what the never-ending apathy of the "good people" has done to the Negroes' minds; there are limits to what can be endured and the good respectable people of our country have pushed these limits dangerously. Going along with Denis de Rougemont, perhaps we might say the Devil is doing his most efficient work in the local churches and in pleasant, well-bred homes.

Here is the big danger. Here is the place where we must take care that we do not criticize the whole movement because of a few half-mad, foolish people who have lost their inner control and good judgment.

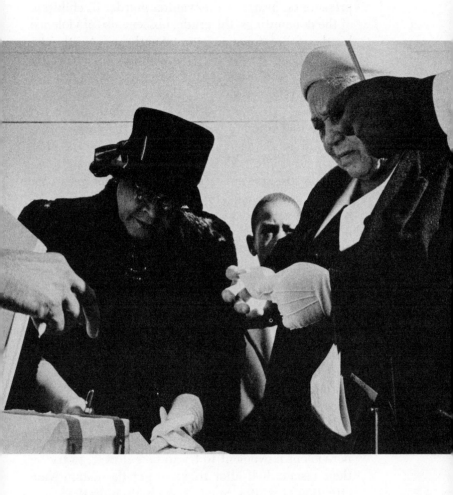

We cannot let ourselves underestimate the heavy pressure on hearts of the wanton murder of children, of the dynamitings, the crude, obscene use of violence by the police force in cities, South and North; the never-ending insults and humiliations broadcast by politicians and other vested interests. "We take and take and take and take . . . day comes we can't take any more." Dr. Sam's words* are haunting us now.

To criticize today without taking the entire situation into honest account, without measuring the little that most white people do to alleviate the suffering and the stress, is an irresponsible act. One prays for reason, one appeals to the conscience—and sometimes, the answer is so small and sometimes, there is no answer. The Negro Movement (with its thousands of white helpers) would like to speak softly; it wants to be reasonable but the noise of white goons, white politicians, white Citizens' Councils, Birch Societies have forced its followers to raise their voices; the dynamitings, the dogs, the electric cattle prods, the fire hose, the long imprisonments for a few minutes of picketing, the vicious treatment given in some of the jails, the exorbitant bonds, the fantastic waits in prison without even preliminary trials, the obscene needling of girl students by policemen, the sadistic judges—this intransigence of whites is now forcing a few desperate Negroes who are intruders in the nonviolent movement to try to take it over, to try by their insane, half-idiot tricks to get the nation-wide attention of whites. Small, sick children do the same;

* *Strange Fruit.* 1944.

but the Movement is no place for the sick or the stupid or the immature, or the sleazy-minded.

What can be done?

An old Negro preacher, evicted with thousands of other sharecroppers in the Delta, long ago in that bleak winter of 1940, met in a little church in Arkansas with a group of whites and Negroes to see what could be done. There were complaints, accusations; there was also a power struggle going on among those who had come "to help." Finally, after a song, the old man was asked to pray. Standing still and silent until the little church was still and silent, he pressed his old hands against the chair he leaned on and said, "Break their hearts, O God; give them tears."

Give us tears. . . . Ah, that is it: how to break our hearts without breaking the unity of this country, the inner conciliation that must never be weakened. How to appeal? How to level walls without the consent that comes from good personal relationships? how to have good relationships while walls stand? How to turn on lights in imaginations so that we can see the little things building into the big ones. These are the unanswered questions.

I have not ended the story for there is no end. This Movement is alive, it is growing, it has already become a part of our life as Americans; it is joyous, still a singing movement, still one full of compassion and love; and being so, it is flexible, amenable to the best our minds and hearts can offer it. Amenable also to the worst we offer it. A brave vigorous movement

127

that is here to stay: rich with infinite creative possibilities, potent—and dangerous, for the potential good can be distorted and lost by the despairing restlessness of those from the ghettos who have no hope, and who are too uninformed historically, too unsure emotionally to analyze current conditions or foresee the consequences of their acts. We, as a people, could be confronted soon by a series of catastrophes. Whether this happens depends on the wisdom of responsible Negroes but more, much more on what every responsible white American does next. One thing is certain in a plexus of uncertainties and that is, our encounter with the future cannot be evaded, it must be met by both the artist and the scientist in us, by our deep intuitions and our rigorously proved knowledge—and by the human being in us, too, that creature who knows the power of compassion, the potency of a strange love that keeps reaching out to bind one man to another.